Wee Sing®

And Move

by
Pamela Conn Beall and
Susan Hagen Nipp

illustrated by
Nancy Spence Klein

PSS!
PRICE STERN SLOAN

To our grandchildren—our delight and inspiration

Cover illustration copyright © 2009 by Liisa Chauncy Guida.
Typesetting and engraving for Wee Sing for Halloween, Wee Sing and Play, Wee Sing The Best of Wee Sing, and Wee Sing and Pretend by Sherry Macy Lines, Curves & Dots Graphics
Typesetting and engraving for Wee Sing Animals, Animals, Animals by Charles Gravenhorst, ProScore Music Engraving
Typesetting and engraving for Wee Sing Games, Games, Games by Brian Healey

 Published by Price Stern Sloan, a division of Penguin Young Readers Group, 345 Hudson Street, New York, NY 10014.
Manufactured in China. CD produced in Singapore.

ISBN 978-0-8431-8959-9
Special Markets ISBN 978-0-8431-7076-4 10 9 8 7 6 5 4 3 2 1

PREFACE

Music and movement are invaluable to the overall development of a child. Songs that get kids up and moving not only provide a great way for them to exercise, but also help to enhance their coordination and learning skills.

Circle games and moving in a line help a child's visual and spatial development; singing the lyrics to a melody gives a sense of pitch and aids in language development; rhythm and rhyme gained through music are valuable pre-reading skills; moving to the directions of the songs helps with concepts such as left and right, up and down, backward and forward, and in and out.

Many of these action songs include doing basic body movements such as walking, running, skipping, hopping, jumping, and galloping. Other motor skills like marching, bending, reaching, and trotting also give children a sense of what their bodies can do. When they master these motions, they gain coordination skills and a confidence that carries over into other areas of learning.

We hope this collection from various *Wee Sing* books gets your child up and moving. Basic skills are certainly being developed but most importantly, we want children to just enjoy singing and moving to the music. So, let's join them as *Wee Sing and Move*.

Pam Beall
Susan Nipp

TABLE OF CONTENTS

CIRCLE AROUND

LISTEN AND MOVE

MOVE WITH IMAGINATION

LINE UP, LET'S GO

LOOBY LOO

Traditional

(Repeat chorus after each verse.)

2. . . . left hand . . .
3. . . . right foot . . .
4. . . . left foot . . .
5. . . . head . . .
6. . . . whole self . . .

Formation:
Children stand in a circle, hands joined.

Action:
- Children circle around on the chorus.
- On the verses, they stop circling and do the actions by putting hand, foot, etc. inside, then outside, then back inside the circle.

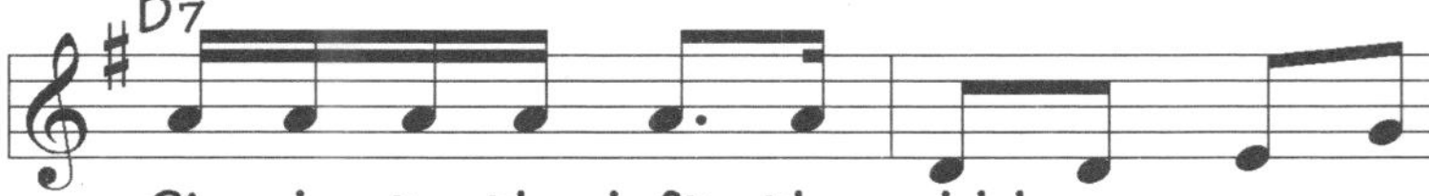

2. Circle to the right, the old brass wagon . . .
3. Everybody in . . .
4. Everybody out . . .

Formation:
Children stand in a circle, hands joined.

Action:
Verses 1 and 2
- Follow directions of the song.

Verse 3
- Children walk to the center of the circle, moving hands forward and up.

Verse 4
- Children walk backward, extending their hands to the rear.
- At the conclusion of the song, everyone bows.

Suggestion:
Children make up their own directions (e.g., tiptoe, skip, hop, . . .).

POP! GOES THE WEASEL

Traditional

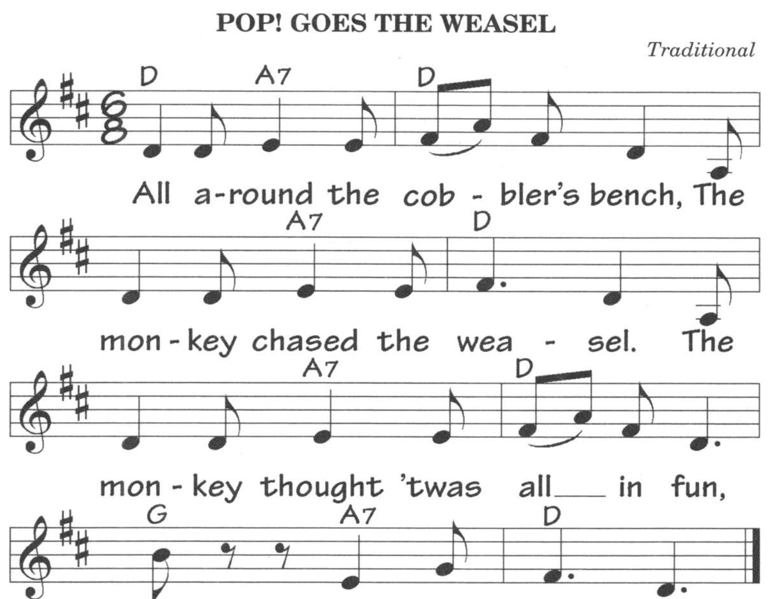

Formation:
Children stand in a circle, hands joined.

Action:
- Children circle around.
- On "POP!" children jump up and land in squatting position.
- Repeat, circling faster each time.

SALLY GO ROUND THE SUN

Formation:
Children stand in a circle, hands joined.

Action:

- Children circle around.
- On "BOOM!" children jump up and reverse direction to immediately start circling and singing the song again.

PUNCHINELLO

Traditional

1. What can you do, Pun-chi-nel-lo fun-ny fel-low?

What can you do, Pun-chi-nel-lo fun-ny you?

2. We can do it, too . . .
3. You choose one of us . . .

Formation:
Children stand in a circle, one child in the center as *Punchinello*.

Action:
Verse 1
- *Punchinello* makes a motion as the others sing.

Verse 2
- Children in the circle copy *Punchinello*'s motion.

Verse 3
- *Punchinello* chooses another child to be in the center and takes that child's place in the circle.

THE MERRY-GO-ROUND

(Tune: Mulberry Bush)

Traditional

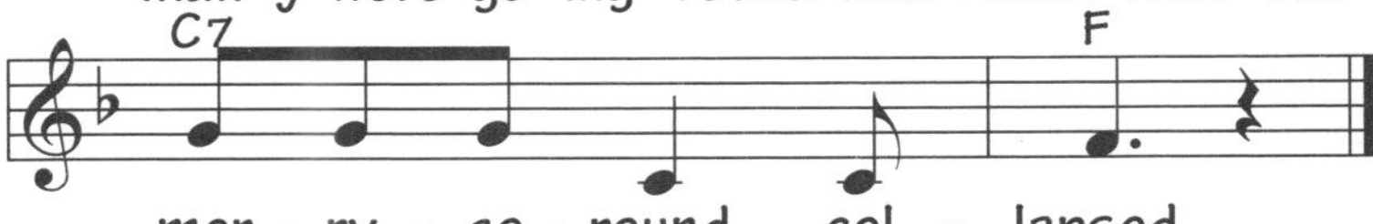

Formation:
Children stand in a circle, hands joined.

Action:
- Children circle around.
- On "collapsed," children fall down.

RING AROUND THE ROSY

England, 1665

2. Tiptoe round the rosy . . .
3. Skip . . .
4. Hop . . .
5. Run . . .

Formation:
Children stand in a circle, hands joined.

Action:
Follow the actions of the words.

THE HOKEY POKEY

Traditional

1. You put your right hand in, you put your right hand out,

You put your right hand in, and you shake it all a-

bout, You do the ho-key po-key, and you

(bend elbows, point index fingers up, sway hips)

turn your-self a-round, That's what it's all a-bout!

(clap in rhythm)

2. You put your left hand in . . .
3. . . . right foot in . . .
4. . . . left foot in . . .
5. . . . right shoulder in . . .
6. . . . left shoulder in . . .
7. . . . right hip in . . .
8. . . . left hip in . . .
9. . . . head in . . .
10. . . . whole self in . . .

Formation:
Children stand in a circle.

Action:
Follow the actions of the words.

JIM ALONG, JOSIE

2. Jump, Jim along, Jim along, Josie,
   Jump, Jim along, Jim along, Joe.
   Jump, Jim along, Jim along, Josie,
   Jump, Jim along, Jim along, Joe.

3. Tiptoe . . .

4. Skate . . .

5. March . . .

(Repeat chorus after each verse.)

Formation:

Children stand in a circle, hands joined.

Action:

- On the verse, children circle around as the words indicate (walk, jump, etc.).
- On the chorus, stop circling, face the center of the circle, and do the actions indicated.

THE TOY SHOP AT MIDNIGHT

The toys in the toy shop are silent all day,
But when it is midnight, they all start to play.

The little tin soldier marches quite stiffly . . .
(Herbert: *March of the Toys* from *Babes in Toyland* – 1903)

The fluffy, old rag doll flops as she walks . . .
(Vivaldi: *The Four Seasons, Autumn; Allegro* – 1725)

The small ballerina twirls on her toes . . .
(Tchaikovsky: *Waltz of the Flowers* from *The Nutcracker* – 1892)

The mechanical robot moves with a jerk . . .
(Debussy: *Golliwogg's Cakewalk* from *Children's Corner* – 1908)

The big, cuddly teddy bear dances quite clumsily . . .
(Tchaikovsky: *Piano Concerto No. 1 in B Flat minor, 1st Movement* – 1875)

But just as the sun starts to peek o'er the hill,
The toys take their places and once more are still.
(Grieg: *Morning* from *Peer Gynt* – 1876)

Susan Nipp

REACH FOR THE SKY

Formation:
Children stand.

Action:
Follow the actions of the words.

PETER HAMMERS

Traditional

2. Peter hammers with two hammers ...
3. ... three hammers ...
4. ... four hammers ...
5. ... five hammers ...
6. Peter's very tired now ...

Formation:
Children sit on the floor or on chairs.

Action:
- *Verse 1* Children pound one fist on floor or leg.
- *Verse 2* Children pound two fists.
- *Verse 3* . . . two fists, one foot.
- *Verse 4* . . . two fists, two feet.
- *Verse 5* . . . two fists, two feet, nod head up and down.
- *Verse 6* Children rub eyes, then lay head on hands.

HEY, MR. KNICKERBOCKER

(Rhythmic Chant)

Hey, Mr. Knickerbocker, bobbity bop,
I feel so good with my bobbity bop,
I put that beat right into my feet!
(stomp feet in rhythm)

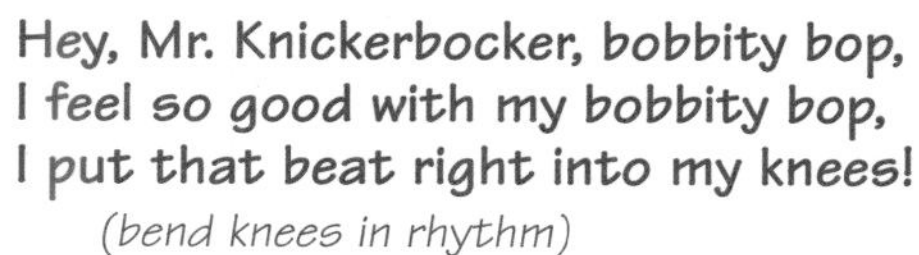

Hey, Mr. Knickerbocker, bobbity bop,
I feel so good with my bobbity bop,
I put that beat right into my knees!
(bend knees in rhythm)

Hey, Mr. Knickerbocker, bobbity bop,
I feel so good with my bobbity bop,
I put that beat right into my hips!
(sway hips in rhythm)

Hey, Mr. Knickerbocker, bobbity bop,
I feel so good with my bobbity bop,
I put that beat right into my shoulders!
(raise and lower shoulders in rhythm)

Hey, Mr. Knickerbocker, bobbity bop,
I feel so good with my bobbity bop,
I put that beat right into my hands!
(shake hands in rhythm)

Hey, Mr. Knickerbocker, bobbity bop,
I feel so good with my bobbity bop,
I put that beat right into my head!
(nod head in rhythm)

Hey, Mr. Knickerbocker, bobbity bop,
I feel so good with my bobbity bop,
I put that beat right into my WHOLE body!
(move whole body in rhythm)

Hey, Mr. Knickerbocker, bobbity bop,
I feel so good with my bobbity bop,
I think I'll STOP!

Traditional

Formation:

Children stand.

Action:

- During verse one, children snap fingers or clap hands in rhythm.
- On the word "feet," children stop snapping or clapping and point to feet. Then they stomp feet in rhythm, continuing through the second verse.
- On the word "knees," children point to knees. Then they bend knees in rhythm, continuing through the third verse.
- Children continue the chant in the same manner, moving the beat to different body parts.

AIRPLANE

Susan Nipp
Susan Nipp
Cm
G7
Sit-ting in the cock-pit of my air-plane,
Cm
Start-ing en-gine num-ber one, Start-ing en-gine
Fm
G7
num-ber two, Rum - ble,
Cm
G7
Mov-ing down the run-way, fast-er and fast-er,
Cm
Fm
Mov-ing down the run-way, fast-er and fast-er,
G7
C
F
Lift off! Fly - ing, fly - ing up in the

G7 C
sky, Fly - ing, fly - ing, I'm up so high,
F C F
Lift-ing up, div-ing down, Bank-ing left,
C G7 C
bank-ing right, Fly-ing, fly-ing, high in the sky.
Fm G7
Run - way in sight, flaps down,
C F C G7
Glid - ing, glid - ing, glid - ing down.
Dm C G7 C
Glid - ing, glid - ing, now it's touch - down.

HEAD AND SHOULDERS CHANT

1. Head and shoulders, baby,
   One, two, three.
   Head and shoulders, baby,
   One, two, three.
   Head and shoulders,
   Head and shoulders,
   Head and shoulders, baby,
   One, two, three.
2. Knees and ankles, baby . . .
3. Turn around, baby . . .
4. Touch the ground, baby . . .

Traditional

Formation:
Children stand.

Action:
- Child touches the body parts when they are chanted.
- Clap on "One, two, three."

HEAD AND SHOULDERS

Traditional

Action:
Touch the different parts of the body when singing about them.

Suggestion:
- Repeat the song, omitting the word *head* throughout, but do the action.
- Repeat again, omitting *head and shoulders* throughout, but do the actions.
- Continue as above until silently doing all the actions.

WALKING, WALKING

(Tune: Are You Sleeping?)

Traditional

Action:
Children follow the actions of the words.

TEDDY BEAR

Traditional

2. Teddy Bear, Teddy Bear, go upstairs,
   Teddy Bear, Teddy Bear, say your prayers,
   Teddy Bear, Teddy Bear, switch off the light,
   Teddy Bear, Teddy Bear, say, "Good-night."

Action:
Children follow the actions of the words.

THE LAND OF SLOW MOTION

Susan Nipp *Susan Nipp*

(Chorus—spoken slowly)

I get out of bed . . .
And brush my teeth . . .
Put on my clothes . . .
And have something to eat . . .

I run outside . . .
And play catch with my brother . . .
I ride my bike . . .
Then swim with my sister . . .

I jump over rocks . . .
And climb a tree . . .
Then run back home . . .
And eat with my family . . .

I put on my pajamas . . .
And brush my teeth . . .
I go to bed . . .
And fall right to sleep.

(Verse—spoken quickly)

2. I'm waking up in the Land of Fast Motion,
Land of Fast Motion, Land of Fast Motion,
I'm waking up in the Land of Fast Motion,
And I can hardly stop.

(Repeat chorus—spoken quickly)

Action:
Pantomime the words.

ANIMAL ACTION

Move to the rhythm, move to the beat,
Move your body, and move your feet.

Birds fly,
Rabbits hop,
Fish swim,
Frogs kerplop!

Ants march,
Worms wiggle,
Peacocks strut,
Jellyfish jiggle.

Move to the rhythm, move to the beat,
Move your body and move your feet.

Monkeys swing,
Lions stalk,
Eagles soar,
People walk.

Penguins waddle,
Kangaroos jump,
Mice scurry,
Camels galumph.

Move to the rhythm, move to the beat,
Move your body and move your feet.

Pam Beall

A WALK THROUGH THE FOREST

One day little Chipper Chipmunk peeked through my window. He blinked at me as though asking me to play. I hurried outside to find him and he began to scamper away.

We ran through the meadow.
(Vivaldi: *Flute Concerto in G Minor, "LaNotte," Allegro* – 1731)

We skipped down the forest trail.
(Rimsky-Korsakov: *Alborado* from *Cappriccio Espagnol* – 1892

We balanced on a log over the rushing stream.
(Sibelius: *Finlandia* – 1899)

We tiptoed past sleeping Mr. Porcupine.
(Bach: *Air on G String* from *Suite No. 3 in D* – 1727)

We hopped around the trees with Missy Rabbit.
(Tchaikovsky: *Polonaise* from *Eugene Onegin* – 1878)

We twirled with the leaves as they fell from the trees.
(Grieg: *Morning* from *Peer Gynt* – 1876)

We helped the ants carry their heavy picnic baskets slowly to the sandy beach.

(Elgar: *Pomp and Circumstance, March No. 1* – 1901)

After the picnic, we played and danced with the ants.

(Bizet: *Les Toreadors* from *Carmen* – 1875)

We waved good-bye to the ants and continued down the path.

We came to a dark tunnel and crawled through it.

(Handel: *Largo* from *Xerxes* – 1734)

I came out of the tunnel and couldn't find Chipper. What happened? I went to look for him.

(Beethoven: *Symphony No. 5, 1st Movement* – 1885)

Hooray! I found him playfully hiding behind a bush. We laughed and called our forest friends to join us as we danced wildly.

(J. Strauss II: *Tritsch Tratsch Polka* – 1858)

As we thought about our wonderful day, we happily marched back home.

(Purcell: *Trumpet Tune* – 1685)

Susan Nipp

THE FREEZE GAME

(Tune: "Rocka My Soul")

Susan Nipp | *Music Adapted: Susan Nipp*

Formation:
Children stand randomly in a large space.

Action:
- Children dance freely during the music.
- Children freeze in position on the word "FREEZE!"

THE LAND OF SILLY

Words Adapted:
Susan Nipp

Traditional

F
Shool, shool, shool I rool,
C7 F C7
Shool I shag-a-rack shool-a-bob-a-loo, In the
F B♭
Land of Sil-ly with a nil-ly wil-ly we, With a
F C7 F
bib - a - lob - a - loo bo beel.

THE DANCE CONTEST

Nancy Klein *Nancy Klein*

2. Denny whirled and twirled and held nothing back,
   He leaped and pranced till the dance floor cracked.
   The judges tied a blue ribbon on his tail
   And gave him eight point five on the Richter Scale.

   (Repeat chorus)

THE DINOSAUR PARTY

Nancy Klein *Susan Nipp*

2. Heads did bob and tails did shake,
It felt just like a big earthquake.
They asked me to join in the fun,
And so we danced till day was done.

Action:
Verses 1 and 2:

- Children snap fingers or clap hands on beats one and three.

Chorus:

- Brontosaurus Boogie: Pointer fingers above head, move to the rhythm.
- Stegosaurus Stomp: Stomp feet to the rhythm, lifting knees high.
- Allosaurus Wiggle: Wiggle hips to the rhythm.
- Tyrannosaurus Romp: Lean backward and forward, hands formed like claws, feet stomping to the beat.

I'm a huge brontosaurus dinosaur, stomping around on the ground!

BRONTOSAURUS

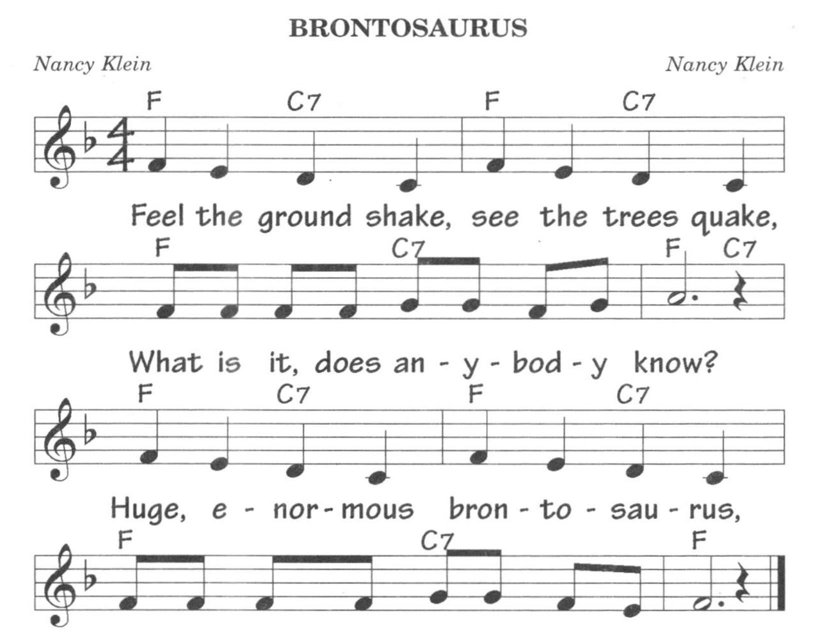

I can soar high in the sky. I'm a big flying reptile, a pteranodon!

PTERANODON

I'm a dinosaur with long legs and I can run very fast. I'm an ornithomimus!

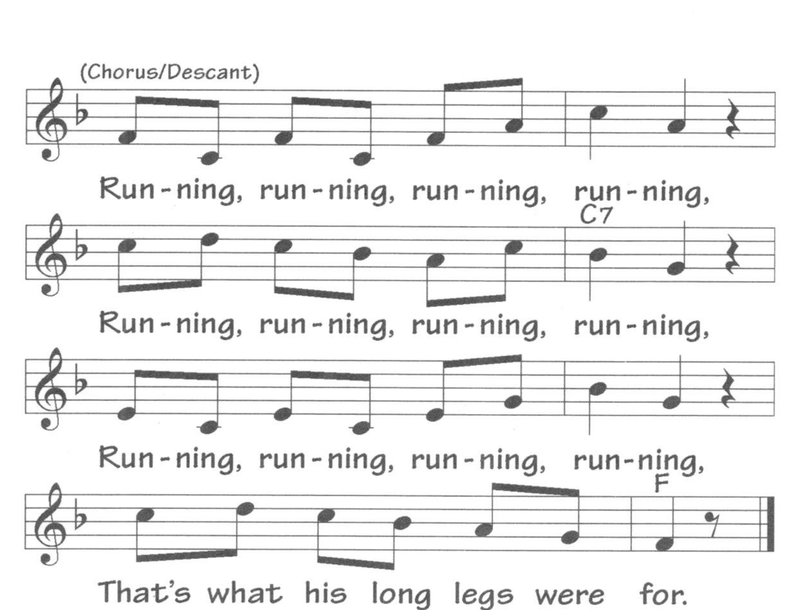
(Chorus/Descant)
Run - ning, run - ning, run - ning, run - ning,
C7
Run - ning, run - ning, run - ning, run - ning,
Run - ning, run - ning, run - ning, run - ning,
F
That's what his long legs were for.

The Cowboy

I'm a cowboy and this is my horse, Old Paint.

All right, Old Paint, I'll brush you down a bit.

Here, have some oats.

Now, I'll put on the saddle.

Hold still, boy, while I get on.

All right, Old Paint, let's start walking down the trail.

2. The hard, hard ground will be my bed,
And the saddle seat will hold my head.

Okay, Old Paint, let's trot along a bit faster.

THE OLD CHISHOLM TRAIL

2. I'm up in the mornin' before daylight,
And before I sleep, the moon shines bright.

(Repeat chorus)

Ready, Old Paint? Let's gallop!

(Rossini: *William Tell Overture* — 1829)

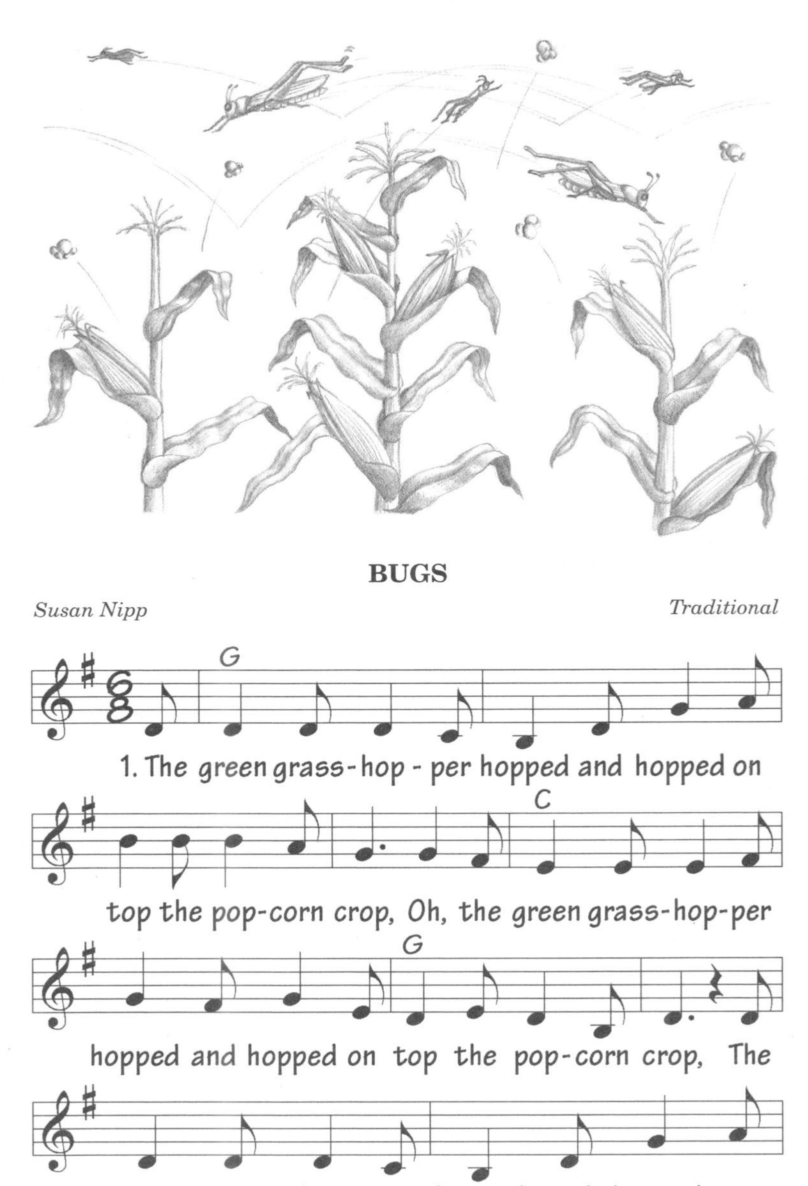
BUGS
Susan Nipp
Traditional
G
1. The green grass-hop - per hopped and hopped on
C
top the pop-corn crop, Oh, the green grass-hop-per
G
hopped and hopped on top the pop-corn crop, The
green grass - hop - per hopped and hopped on

top the pop-corn crop, Oh, the green grass-hop-per

hopped and hopped on top the pop - corn crop.

2. The inchworm arched and inched his way along the brownish branch . . .
3. The dragonfly flew fast for fun while flitting on four wings . . .
4. The red ants hurried as they scurried all around the ground . . .
5. I sat on the ants and got ants in my pants and ran fast to get rid of the ants . . .

POPCORN BALL

Action:
Children pretend to be corn, popping.

RACE CAR

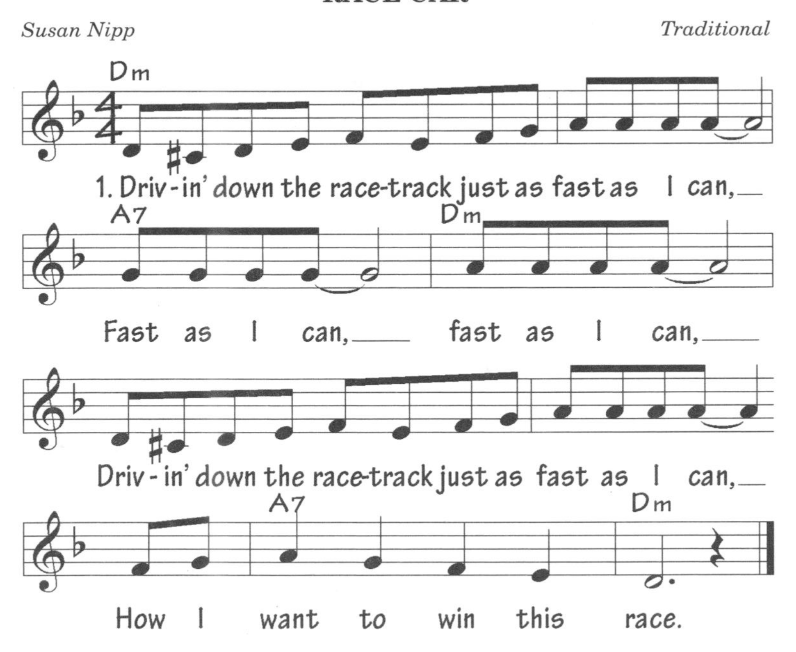
Susan Nipp
Traditional
Dm
1. Driv-in' down the race-track just as fast as I can,
A7
Dm
Fast as I can, fast as I can,
Driv-in' down the race-track just as fast as I can,
A7
Dm
How I want to win this race.

Turn to the left!

Turn to the right!

Slam on the brakes!

Whoa, I'm spinning around!

Whew! I'm back on the track and racing for the finish line!

2. Drivin' down the racetrack just as fast as I can,
Fast as I can, fast as I can,
Drivin' down the racetrack just as fast as I can,
It's the checkered flag, *I WIN!*

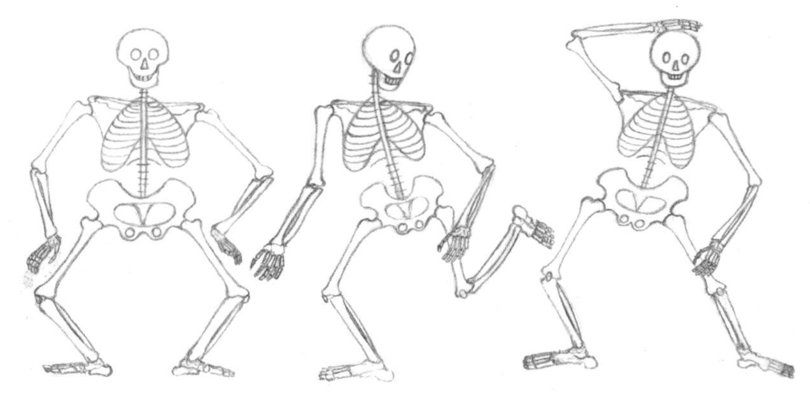

BONES

My bones make up my skeleton,
Which is the frame of me,
And though you cannot see them,
My bones move easily.

For I can leap and twist and creep
And run and sway and jiggle
And bend and slide and hop and glide
And bounce and roll and wiggle.

Susan Nipp

(Saint-Saëns: *Danse Macabre* – 1875)

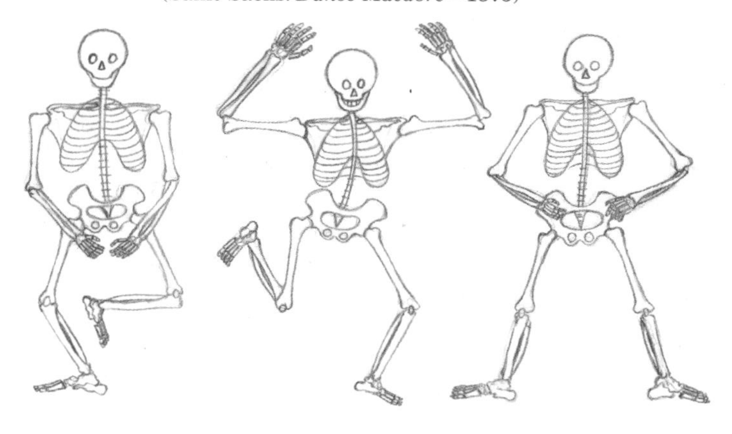

FOLLOW ME

Formation:
Children stand in a line, single file. One child is the leader.

Action:

- As the leader moves around the room doing a specific action such as clapping hands, tapping head, flying, etc., the children follow the leader and copy the actions.
- When the verse is finished, the leader goes to the end of the line and the next child becomes the leader. (On the audio there is a musical cue.)
- Continue until all have been the leader.

MARCH

Attention!
March in place, 2, 3, 4!
Left, right, left, right, left, right, left!
Forward . . . march, 2, 3, 4,
1, 2, 3, 4!

To the left . . . march!

To the right . . . march!

To the rear . . . march!

Attention, 2, 3, 4,
1, 2, 3, 4,
Ready . . . stop!

Susan Nipp

(John Philip Sousa: *The Stars and Stripes Forever*—1897)

HANSEL AND GRETEL DANCE

Formation:

Children stand in a line, single file. Each child holds on to the waist of the child in front of him.

Action:

Children do the following actions as shown in the music:

ⓐ Extend right leg, touching heel to ground.
ⓑ Bend knee, touching right toe to ground.
ⓒ Extend left leg, touching heel to ground.
ⓓ Bend knee, touching left toe to ground.
ⓔ Jump forward once.
ⓕ Jump backward once.
ⓖ Jump forward four times.

THE ANIMAL PARADE

(Tune: "The Washington Post" March)

Susan Nipp *John Philip Sousa, 1889*

(chorus)

2. The armadillo takes his time behind the skunk,
The shy koala rides a fawn,
The parakeet flies by the peacock and the prickly porcupine,
This animal parade goes on and on! And on!

(chorus)

3. The rabbit hops between the frog and kangaroo,
The penguin waddles by the swan,
The ladybug and bumblebee fly high above the crocodile,
This animal parade goes on and on! And on!

INDEX

Discover the entire best-selling line of Wee Sing® books, audio, and DVDs